Novel Experiments With Electricity

by

John Potter Shields

HOWARD W. SAMS & CO., INC.
THE BOBBS-MERRILL CO., INC.
INDIANAPOLIS · KANSAS CITY · NEW YORK

Preface

Electricity and magnetism help to form the "building blocks" of the modern world. While we often take these invisible servants for granted, they are both very fascinating. A good understanding of them can be intriguing and useful. You will learn how all matter is composed of basic building blocks called molecules. A simple discussion will show how these molecules are constructed, and how they are associated with electricity and magnetism.

The book is intended to introduce the myriad of the fascinating properties of electricity and magnetism. In the pages that follow, you will find first a brief introduction to the fundamentals of electricity and magnetism. Secondly, you will find a number of interesting and novel experiments that range from a ground telephone and electric arc to a miniature lightning generator and synchronous motor. To help in the construction of the experiments, the book has been profusely illustrated.

All efforts have been made to keep project costs down. In many cases, the projects can be assembled with parts from your junk box. The parts have been selected so that they are readily available from your local electronics distributors or one of the catalog supply houses.

It is the sincere hope of the author that you will find this book a source of many hours of enjoyment.

JOHN POTTER SHIELDS

Contents

From a Magnetic Field — An Electromagnet — Magnetic
Solenoid — A Magnetic Solenoid Dice Thrower — Magnetic
Sorter — The Bouncing Spring — Induction-Loop Trans-
mitter — Ground Telephone — Sound-Powered Telephone —
Magnetic Shake Table — Variable-Reactance Power Control
— A Magnetic Stirrer — Magnetizer — Demagnetizer —
The Spark Coil — Dancing Polywogs — A Magnetic Metal
Finder — A Novel Synchronous Motor — A Simple Relay

CHAPTER 4

1

Basics of Electricity and Magnetism

Before taking a look at the various experiments and projects described in this book, let us first examine some of the basic properties of electricity and magnetism.

THE NATURE OF ELECTRICITY AND MAGNETISM

Electricity and magnetism go hand-in-hand. Generally, you will not find one without the other. When an electric current is sent through a wire (circuit), a magnetic field is generated around the conductor. Similarly, when a conductor is passed through a magnetic field, an electric current is generated within the wire.

The exact nature of electricity and magnetism is not clearly understood. However, an acceptable explanation of electricity is that it consists of a flow of charged carriers, which are generally electrons. Magnetism is a property possessed by certain materials by which these materials can exert mechanical force on neighboring masses of magnetic materials. A material is said to be magnetized when its molecular domains are all (or nearly all) arranged in orderly fashion—all facing in the same direction.

We shall now take a detailed look at the nature of electricity and magnetism. In order to do this, we must first gain some knowledge of the basic building blocks of matter, namely the *atom* and its components.

THE ATOM AND ITS CONSTRUCTION

All matter is composed of basic building blocks called *molecules*. In turn, these molecules are composed of still smaller particles of matter known as *atoms*. Going still further down the size scale, we find that the atom is made up of still smaller particles—electrons (negatively charged), protons (positively charged), and neutrons (no charge).

A *neutral* atom has an equal number of electrons and protons. An example of this is the simple hydrogen atom diagramed in Fig. 1-1. Notice that this atom has a single electron and a single proton. The proton forms the nucleus of the atom, and the electron orbits about the central nucleus. This arrangement is analogous to our solar system, with its central sun and the orbiting planets.

In the carbon atom, there are 6 protons in its nucleus and 6 orbiting electrons. The main thing to remember is that in a neutral atom, there are always an equal number of electrons and protons.

In an atom, the electrons orbiting nearest the nucleus are tightly bound to the nucleus by the attractive force of the protons in the central nucleus. The reason for this attraction is that the protons carry a positive net electric charge, while the electrons carry a negative net electric charge. Thus, since opposite electric charges attract each other, the orbiting electrons will be bound to the nucleus.

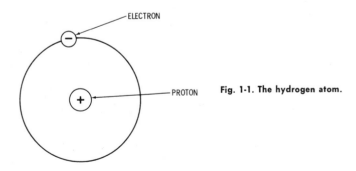

Fig. 1-1. The hydrogen atom.

Electrons orbiting the central nucleus are arranged in discrete rings around the nucleus. The outermost ring of electrons is named the *valence ring,* while the electrons within this ring are called *valence electrons.*

Atoms such as copper and aluminum have relatively few valence electrons. These few valence electrons may be easily stripped away from the attractive force of the nucleus by external forces. By contrast, if an atom has a large number of valence electrons, the valence electrons will be tightly bound to the central nucleus, and it will be extremely difficult to remove them by an external force.

When an electron has been removed from the valence ring of an atom, it becomes a *free* electron, and can move about from atom to atom. This movement or flow of free electrons constitutes a flow of electric current.

POSITIVE AND NEGATIVE ELECTRIC CHARGES

As illustrated in Fig. 1-2, when a glass rod is rubbed with a silk cloth, some of the valence electrons in the glass atoms will be transferred to the silk cloth by the process of friction. As a result, the glass rod acquires a net positive charge, and the cloth assumes a negative net electric charge. If a hard rubber or bakelite rod is rubbed with a wool cloth, a few of the electrons from the cloth will be transferred to the rod. As a result, the rod acquires a negative net electric charge.

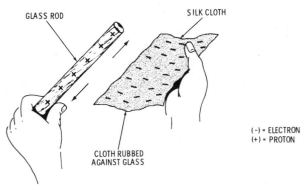

Fig. 1-2. Glass rod acquires positive charge.

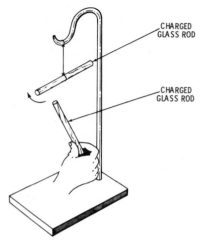

CHARGED
GLASS ROD

CHARGED
GLASS ROD

Fig. 1-3. Like electric charges repel
each other.

Refer to Fig. 1-3, which shows a glass rod suspended by a string so that the rod can move freely. Assume that the glass rod has been rubbed with a silk cloth and has acquired a positive electric charge. When a second charged glass rod is brought near the suspended rod, the suspended rod swings away. This indicates that similar electric charges repel each other.

If a negatively charged bakelite rod is brought near the suspended positively charged glass rod as shown in Fig. 1-4, the glass rod is attracted to the bakelite rod, indicating that dissimilar electric charges attract each other.

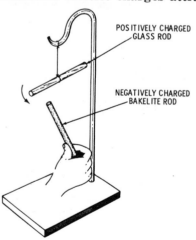

POSITIVELY CHARGED
GLASS ROD

NEGATIVELY CHARGED
BAKELITE ROD

Fig. 1-4. Unlike electric charges
attract each other.

STATIC ELECTRICITY

The examples of charged bodies previously outlined represent static electric charges. That is, the bodies acquire an electric charge that remains stationary on the body until it leaks off or is dissipated by some other means.

Perhaps one of the most familiar forms of static electricity is lightning. Due to friction, minute electric charges accumulate on water droplets as they are carried aloft by strong wind currents. These droplets accumulate to form clouds, and the combined electric charges form a very large electric charge. The discharge between clouds or between the clouds and earth causes the lightning.

THE ELECTROSTATIC FIELD

Earlier, we saw how a charged rod could attract or repel a suspended rod depending upon the relative electric charges between the two rods. This action of attraction or repulsion between the two rods is the result of electrostatic fields surrounding the two rods.

The electrostatic fields around a charged body are often represented by *lines of force*. These lines indicate intensity and direction of the force, and the general shape of the field. The direction is indicated by arrow heads, and intensity is denoted by the number of lines. A method agreed on by scientists uses a small positive charge to test direction of the field. They concluded that the direction of the field is away from a positive charge, and toward for a negative charge. This is the direction a positive test charge would take according to the law that like charges repel and unlike charges attract Fig. 1-5A shows the direction of the electrostatic field around a positive charge, and Fig. 1-5B shows the direction of the field around a negative charge.

DYNAMIC ELECTRICITY

In our discussion of static electricity, the electric charges acquired by the bodies remained stationary until they leaked off or were discharged. By contrast, *dynamic* electricity

(A) Positive charge.

(B) Negative charge.

Fig. 1-5. Direction of electrostatic fields around charges of static electricity.

deals with the movement of electrically charged particles, which are most commonly electrons.

In order to establish a flow of free electrons through a conductor, it is necessary that the conductor be connected to two points of different electrical potential. For example, if a conductor is connected between a positively charged body and a negatively charged body, electrons will flow from the negatively charged body to the positively charged body through the conductor. This flow ceases when the charges on the two bodies have been reduced to zero.

ELECTRICAL UNITS

In order to produce a flow of free electrons through a conductor and thus establish a flow of electric current, a potential difference must exist between the ends of the conductor. This potential difference is expressed in units called *volts*. A volt is equivalent to the force required to produce a current of 1 ampere through a resistance of 1 ohm. In a sense, the volt may be considered as a unit of electrical pressure.

The flow of electric current is measured in *amperes*. One volt across 1 ohm of resistance causes a current of 1 ampere.

The resistance offered by a conductor to the flow of current through it is measured in *ohms*. One ohm is the value of resistance through which a potential difference of 1 volt will maintain a current of 1 ampere.

OHM'S LAW

There is a definite relationship between the volt, ohm, and ampere. This relationship is expressed by Ohm's Law.

Ohm's law states that the voltage across an element of a dc circuit is equal to the current in amperes through the element, multiplied by the resistance of the element in ohms. It is expressed mathematically as:

$$E = I \times R$$

where,

E is the voltage in volts,
I is the current in amperes,
R is the resistance in ohms.

The other two equations obtained by transposition are:

$$I = \frac{E}{R}$$

and

$$R = \frac{E}{I}$$

METHODS OF PRODUCING ELECTRICITY

There are a number of methods of producing electricity. The electrochemical battery is the most common example of the production of electrical energy by chemical means. When two dissimilar metals are placed in a chemical electrolyte, a potential (voltage) difference develops across the metals.

Electricity can also be produced by friction. As described earlier, when certain materials are rubbed together, the resulting friction will produce an electric charge.

When a conductor is passed through a magnetic field, an electric current is induced in the conductor. The strength of this current is determined by the strength of the magnetic field through which the conductor is passed, and the speed at which the conductor is passed through the magnetic field.

It is also possible to produce an electric current by heating two dissimilar metals. Such an arrangement is called a *thermocouple*.

Certain substances have the property of generating an electrical voltage when pressure is applied to them. This is known as the *piezoelectric effect*. A good example of this is the common "crystal" phono cartridge.

When light strikes certain materials, a voltage is developed across the terminals of the material. This *photoelectric effect* is made use of in the photoelectric cell.

MAGNETISM AND MAGNETS

Any material that has the property of attracting ferrous metals is called a magnet, and it is this property that is known as magnetism. The effects of magnetism were known many centuries ago. It has been said that the Chinese were aware of its effects as early as 2000 B.C. In fact, the first magnetic compass was developed by the Chinese.

There are two basic types of magnets—natural and artificial. An example of a natural magnet is the *lodestone,* which is a special form of iron oxide called *magnetite.* Artificial magnets are now used in place of natural magnets, since they can be made with much greater magnetic power.

Artificial magnets may be classified into two basic types— *temporary* and *permanent.* Temporary magnets lose almost all of their magnetism when they are removed from the magnetizing force. Permanent magnets will retain their magnetism after the magnetizing force has been removed. Permanent magnets are used in such devices as loudspeakers, headphones, motors, etc.

Magnetic Properties

If a piece of ferrous material, such as steel, is magnetized, it now has magnetic poles, as shown in Fig. 1-6. One end is the *north* pole, while the other end is the *south* pole.

If a magnet is suspended by a string so that it can rotate freely, and the north pole of a second magnet is brought near the north pole of the suspended magnet, the suspended magnet will swing away from the other magnet, as shown in Fig. 1-7A. On the other hand, if the south pole of the

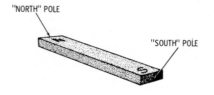

"NORTH" POLE

"SOUTH" POLE

Fig. 1-6. Magnetic poles of a magnet.

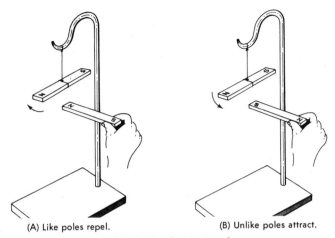

(A) Like poles repel.   (B) Unlike poles attract.

Fig. 1-7. Action of magnetic poles.

second magnet is brought near the north pole of the suspended magnet, the suspended magnet will swing toward the other magnet. This is shown in Fig. 1-7B. From this, it can be seen that opposite magnetic poles attract, while identical magnetic poles repel.

The Theory of Magnetism

Although the complete "why" of magnetism is not exactly understood, a satisfactory explanation follows. The molecular theory of magnetism is the most widely accepted theory of magnetism. In this theory, it is assumed that the molecules of the magnetic material are considered as tiny magnets.

Fig. 1-8A represents a magnetic material that is not magnetized. Note that the molecules are arranged in an orderly fashion. When the material is magnetized, these *molecular domains* are rearranged into an orderly fashion as shown in Fig. 1-8B. The greater the number of molecular domains that become aligned in the same direction, the stronger is

UNMAGNETIZED MATERIAL   MAGNETIZED MATERIAL

(A) Unmagnetized material.   (B) Magnetized material.

Fig. 1-8. Molecular domain alignment.

15

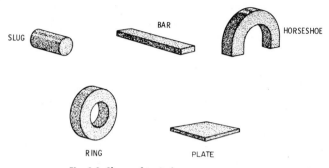

Fig. 1-9. Shape of typical permanent magnets.

the magnetic field of the material. A few typical shapes of magnets are illustrated in Fig. 1-9.

The Magnetic Field

Earlier in this chapter, we saw how a body with an acquired electrostatic charge possessed an electrostatic field around it. Similarly, a magnet has a magnetic field surrounding it.

The strength, or intensity, of the magnetic field surrounding a magnet is expressed in units termed *oersteds*. A magnetic field intensity of one oersted exists when it is capable of exerting a pulling force of one dyne. This can be expressed as follows:

$$F = m \times H$$

where,

F is the force exerted on a magnetic pole placed in a magnetic field,
m is the strength of the unit pole,
H is the magnetic field intensity in oersteds.

Magnetic Induction

If a magnet is brought near ferrous material, the material will become magnetized by magnetic induction. What happens is that some of the magnetic lines of force from one pole of the magnet flow through the steel and to the opposite pole of the magnet. These magnetic lines of force flowing through the material cause it to become magnetized. One property of magnetic induction is that the polarity of the pole (north or south) of the material being magnetized will be opposite to that of the magnetizing magnet at the point of contact.

Some Additional Properties of Magnets and Magnetism

Some additional properties of magnetism and magnets include:

Reluctance—Reluctance refers to the opposition a material offers to applied magnetic lines of force. This term is analogous to electrical resistance.

Permeability—This is the reciprocal of reluctance, and refers to the ability of. a material to conduct magnetic lines of force through it.

Curie Point—This term refers to the temperature at which a heated magnetic material will lose its magnetic properties.

ELECTROMAGNETISM

Electromagnetism involves the use of an electric current to produce a magnetic field. In the year 1819, Hans Christian Oersted made the observation that a magnetic field was produced around a wire carrying an electric current. This effect is illustrated in Fig. 1-10. However, the strength of

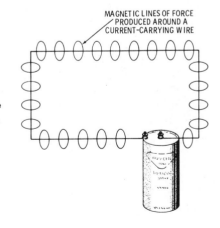

MAGNETIC LINES OF FORCE PRODUCED AROUND A CURRENT-CARRYING WIRE

Fig. 1-10 Magnetic lines of force around a current-carrying wire.

the current in the wire determines the strength of the magnetic field.

When a conductor is wound into a coil, as shown in Fig. 1-11, the effect is to increase the total magnetic field generated around the coil. This is due to the additive effects of the magnetic fields generated around each conducting turn of the coil.

The total strength of the magnetic field produced around the coil is determined by the number of turns in the coil, and the amount of current in the coil.

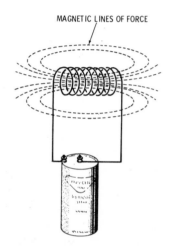

MAGNETIC LINES OF FORCE

Fig. 1-11. Magnetic lines of force around a current-carrying coil.

If the coil is wound over a core made of ferrous material, such as iron or steel, the effective magnetic field strength will be greatly increased. This is because the core tends to concentrate the magnetic lines of force at its ends. Since the core has a lower reluctance than air, the magnetic lines of force will be concentrated at the ends of the core.

The number of turns and the applied current of a coil have a definite relationship, expressed as *ampere-turns*. This relationship is as follows:

$$\text{Ampere-turns} = N \times I$$

where,
N is the number of turns in the coil,
I is the current in amperes through the coil.

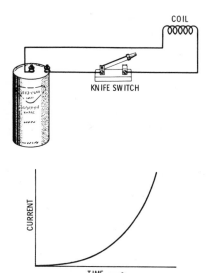

Fig. 1-12. Current build-up through
a coil.

Inductance

Take a look at Fig. 1-12, which shows a coil connected in series with a switch and a battery. When the switch is closed, the battery begins to produce a current in the coil. As a result, a magnetic field is built up around the turns of the coil. This magnetic field induces a *counterelectromotive force* (counter emf) in the turns of the coil in a direction opposite to that of the applied current. This counter emf tends to oppose any change of current in the coil. As the current in the coil approaches maximum, the counter emf gradually decreases until it becomes zero, and full battery current is present in the coil.

The greater the number of turns in the coil, the greater the developed counter emf. Also, if the coil is wound over a ferrous core, the amount of developed counter emf is increased.

The Transformer

One of the most important applications of electromagnetism is the transformer. Fig. 1-13 illustrates the basic operation of the transformer. In operation, when the switch

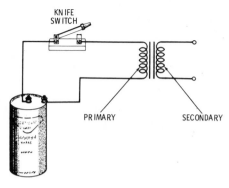

Fig. 1-13. A basic transformer.

is closed, a varying current is introduced into the transformer primary. This current builds up a varying magnetic field around the primary winding. In turn, the magnetic field is coupled by magnetic induction to the secondary winding, where it induces a current. When the current in the primary winding has reached its full value, the magnetic field will no longer be in motion, and current ceases to be generated in the secondary winding. Remember, the current in the primary winding of the transformer must be varying in order for a current to be induced in the secondary winding of the transformer.

Ratio of Primary to Secondary Turns—If the primary of a transformer has a greater number of turns than its secondary, the voltage developed across its secondary terminals will be smaller than the voltage applied to the primary. Such a transformer is called a *step-down* transformer. On the other hand, if the transformer has less turns in its primary than in its secondary, a greater voltage will be developed across its secondary. Such a transformer is termed a *step-up* transformer.

2

Basic Experiments in Electricity

In this chapter, a number of basic experiments in electricity will be described. These experiments will acquaint you with the interesting aspects of the basic electrical law and fundamentals.

A SIMPLE ELECTROSCOPE TO DEMONSTRATE
STATIC ELECTRICITY

An electroscope is a device that is used to show the presence of an electrostatic charge.

Fig. 2-1 shows the basic construction of the electroscope. The required items are a small chemical flask, a cork stopper to fit the mouth of the flask, a 6-inch length of No. 12 or No. 14 solid copper wire, and a small piece of aluminum foil.

Construction of the electroscope is simple. Through the center of the cork stopper pierce a hole just large enough to pass the copper wire through. Pass the wire through the stopper, and make a small right angle hook as shown. At the opposite end of the wire (the part that passes through the top of the stopper), make a small hook. Take the small piece of foil, bend it in two, and place it over the right-angle hook. Finally, insert the cork stopper in the flask. The electroscope is now ready for operation.

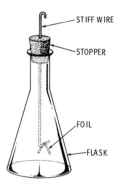

Fig. 2-1. Construction of a simple electroscope.

As shown in Fig. 2-2, place a comb, which you have previously rubbed with a wool cloth, near the hook of the electroscope. Notice that the leaves of the foil will fly apart. The reason for this action is that according to the law of repulsion, the negative charge on the comb repels the free electrons in the hook and drives them down to the leaves of the foil. Because the leaves receive like charges, they spread apart.

Now, touch the hook of the electroscope with the tip of your finger. Note that the ends of the foil slowly close back together indicating that the charge placed on the foil has been drained off.

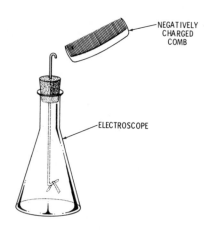

Fig. 2-2. Operation of a simple electroscope.

VAN DE GRAAFF GENERATOR

In the experiment with the electroscope that was just described, the charge of static electricity was generated by rubbing a comb with a wool cloth. By means of a device known as a Van de Graaff generator, it is possible to generate much larger amounts of static electricity.

Fig. 2-3 shows the basic idea of the Van de Graaff generator. A cloth, or rubber, belt is connected between two pulleys located at either end of a long cylinder of an insulating material, such as plastic. The pulley at the lower end of the cylinder is connected to the shaft of a high-speed motor. A wire brush contacts the rotating belt at the lower end of the cylinder. A similar wire brush, cemented to a ball at the upper end of the cylinder, makes contact with the belt at the top of the cylinder.

As the belt rotates, a static charge is developed on it by friction between it and the lower wire brush. At the top of the cylinder, the charge developed on the belt is applied to the ball by means of the metal *collector* brush. As the belt continues to rotate, the electric charge developed on the ball intensifies.

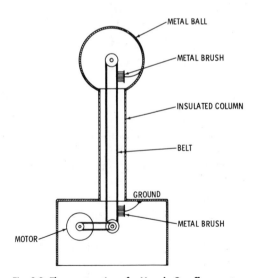

Fig. 2-3. The construction of a Van de Graaff generator.

While it is possible to build your own Van de Graaff generator, the low price of a "ready-made" unit is a better choice, since there is a fair amount of work involved in building one. Lafayette Radio has one such unit. It is called a Novatron and is available under part number 99-E-90086. Fig. 2-4 is an illustration of the Lafayette unit.

To operate the generator, plug the line cord into a 120-volt ac source and place its power switch in the ON position to start the drive motor. The belt will rotate between

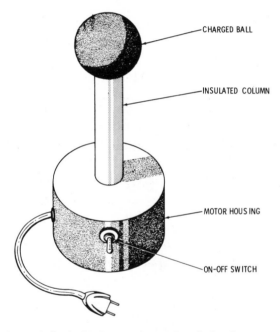

Fig. 2-4. A sketch of Lafayette Novatron (Van de Graaff generator).

the top and bottom rolls. After a few minutes of operation, bring a fingertip near the top metal ball, and a spark will jump over to your finger. Although fairly long sparks can be drawn from the ball, the amount of current involved is so slight that no danger of serious shock is present.

The Lafayette Van de Graaff generator is supplied with a number of accessories for performing a number of novel experiments.

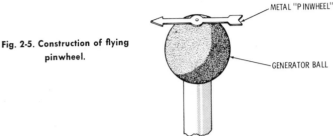

Fig. 2-5. Construction of flying pinwheel.

METAL "PINWHEEL"

GENERATOR BALL

Pinwheel

Fig. 2-5 shows the setup for making a "flying pinwheel." The metal arrow-shaped piece is placed on the ball of the generator and power is applied to the motor. After a few seconds, the arrow-shaped rotor will begin to spin. If you view this in a darkened room, you will notice that a corona discharge appears at the ends of the rotor. It is this corona discharge that causes the spinning of the rotor.

Jumping Balls

A plastic vial containing a number of pith balls is supplied with the Lafayette generator. If you build your own Van de Graaff generator, a satisfactory substitute for the vial would be a small plastic pill bottle; small pieces of cork could substitute for the pith balls. Place this plastic vial with its contents on top of the generator as shown in Fig. 2-6. Apply operating power to the generator; in a few seconds, the pith balls will bounce vigorously up and down inside the plastic vial.

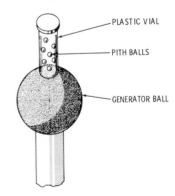

PLASTIC VIAL

PITH BALLS

GENERATOR BALL

Fig. 2-6. Dancing balls experiment.

Fig. 2-7 shows another experiment with the generator. Place a pin through the center of 5 or 6 strips of thin paper, such as tissue paper. Place the pin through the hole in the top of the generator ball, and apply power to the generator. The strips of paper will fly out due to the repulsion of like electric charges at the end of the paper.

For best performance from the Van de Graaff generator, the humidity of the air should be low. For this reason, try to find a place to use the generator where there is not too much moisture in the air. If this is not possible, results can

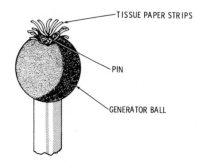

Fig. 2-7. Dancing tissue paper experiment.

be improved by thoroughly drying all parts of the generator. A handy way of doing this is to place the generator in a kitchen oven. Set the oven for a temperature of about 150 degrees.

LEYDEN JAR

The Leyden jar is the earliest form of the "electric condenser," or as we now call it, the capacitor. The Leyden jar was invented in the eighteenth century, and was named after the city where it was invented. It was used to store electrostatic electricity.

Fig. 2-8 shows the construction of a Leyden jar. A layer of metal foil is placed on the inside surface of a glass container. One end of a wire is attached to this foil; the other end of this wire is passed through a hole in the cover of the glass container. The cover is made from an insulative material. The outer surface of the jar is similarly coated with foil.

Fig. 2-8. Construction of a Leyden jar.

WIRE TO INNER FOIL

INSULATED COVER

GLASS JAR

INSIDE FOIL

OUTSIDE FOIL

To use the Leyden jar, connect the output from an electrostatic generator, such as a Van de Graaff generator, between the outer foil and inner foil of the Leyden jar. In operation, when the electrostatic generator is energized, opposite electric charges are built up on the inner and outer foils of the Leyden jar. The amount of these charges increases as the electrostatic generator continues to operate.

When the electrostatic generator is disconnected from the Leyden jar, the Leyden jar is in a "charged" condition; that is, opposite electric charges remain on the inner and outer foils. The Leyden jar will retain its charged condition until it is discharged by connecting a wire between the inner and outer foils.

Constructing a Leyden Jar

A Leyden jar can easily be constructed. Use a straight-sided glass jar, such as an olive or peanut butter jar. Cut out a strip of aluminum foil with a width about ⅔ the height of the jar. The length of the foil should be sufficient to go completely around the circumference of the jar. Secure the foil strip to the inner surface of the jar by means of an adhesive, such as radio service cement or rubber cement. In a similar manner, cut a strip of foil with the same dimensions and secure it to the outer surface of the jar.

There are several ways of making a lid for the jar. The lid must be a good insulator, such as wood or plastic. If you have a wood-turning lathe, you can make a good fitting wooden lid. If you do not have access to a lathe, cut out a round piece of wood with a diameter slightly larger than the top of the jar. This lid can be cemented to the edge of the top of the jar with a good adhesive.

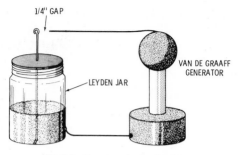

Fig. 2-9. Charging the Leyden jar.

Connection to the inner foil is made by means of a flexible wire. The opposite end of the wire is soldered to a length of stiff copper wire, which is passed through a hole in the jar lid. A small hook is made in the end of the wire.

Using the Leyden Jar

Fig. 2-9 shows how the Leyden jar is charged. Connect a lead from the metal base of the Van de Graaff generator to the outer foil of the Leyden jar. Connect one end of a second lead to the ball of the generator, and position the other end of the wire to form a ¼-inch gap between it and the wire extending from the Leyden jar.

Apply power to the Van de Graaff generator. After a few seconds, you will note a series of sparks jumping across the gap. This sparking will decrease and finally cease. The cessation of sparking indicates that the Leyden jar is charged.

Now refer to Fig. 2-10. Touch one end of a wire to the outer foil of the Leyden jar, and bring the other end of the wire to within about ½ inch of the center wire of the Ley-

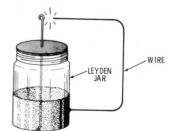

Fig. 2-10. Discharging the Leyden jar.

den jar. A light spark will jump across the gap, discharging the Leyden jar. You will see that this spark is much brighter than the sparks produced from the Van de Graaff generator. This indicates that the Leyden jar has accumulated, or stored, the electrostatic charge in greater quantity than was released by the Van de Graaff generator.

HOMEMADE LIGHT BULB

This interesting experiment demonstrates the basic principle of the incandescent electric light bulb. Fig. 2-11 shows the basic setup for the homemade light bulb. First, obtain a

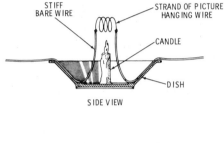

SIDE VIEW

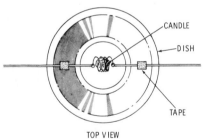

TOP VIEW

Fig. 2-11. Construction of a demonstration light bulb.

flat-bottom dish. In the center of this dish, mount a small candle, such as a birthday cake candle. Drop a few droplets of molten wax on the plate bottom, then stick the candle in the wax while it is still hot.

Next, place two lengths of bare wire along the edges of the dish, down to the bottom, and up at right angles as shown. The wires can be secured in place with drops of candle wax.

Now take a length of picture-hanging wire, and remove one of the strands. Connect this strand between the ends of the two bare wires by wrapping the ends of the strand around the ends of the two bare wires.

Next, connect the ends of the two bare wires coming out from the edge of the dish in series with a 15-ohm, 20-watt rheostat, switch, and 6-volt battery. A lantern battery or four series-connected No. 6 dry cells will do, as shown in Fig. 2-12.

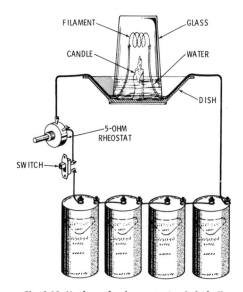

Fig. 2-12. Hookup of a demonstration light bulb.

Finally, partially fill the dish with water, light the candle, and quickly place a glass tumbler over the candle, resting it on the bottom of the dish. The candle will continue to burn for a few moments, then go out. After it goes out, the level of water inside the glass should have risen slightly, indicating that a partial vacuum has been created within the tumbler.

Close the switch and slowly turn the rheostat toward its minimum setting. You will notice that the iron wire will begin to glow with an increasing brilliance as the current through it is increased. If too much current is passed through the filament, its temperature will increase to the point where it will burn out.

Other materials beside the iron picture wire may be tried for the bulb filament. Such materials might be steel wire, or a piece of the tungsten filament salvaged from an old light bulb.

CARBON ARC

The earliest type of electric light was produced by the carbon arc. Fig. 2-13 shows the basic principle of the carbon arc. Two carbon electrodes are connected to a voltage source of approximately 40 to 60 volts. To start (strike) the arc, the two electrodes are momentarily touched together, then are quickly drawn apart. An arc is established between the electrodes. This arc is at a very high temperature—over 5000° F—and produces a very intense blue-white light. The light from the arc is very rich in ultraviolet radiation, so colored glasses or goggles must always be used when viewing the arc.

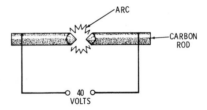

Fig. 2-13. Principle of the carbon arc.

Fig. 2-14 shows the setup for making a demonstration carbon arc. *Never* look directly at the arc produced by this demonstration arc without wearing very dark sun glasses. Actually, a pair of welder's goggles is preferable.

As shown in Fig. 2-14, the two arc electrodes consist of carbon rods salvaged from discarded size "D" flashlight cells. Points are formed on the ends of the rods by sharpening them in an ordinary pencil sharpener. Care must be taken when sharpening the carbon rods, because they are rather brittle.

The sharpened rods are held in position by means of a holder made of sheet-metal clips that are attached to the

31

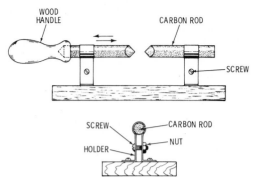

Fig. 2-14. Demonstration carbon arc.

wooden base. One of the carbon rods is held securely in place by one clip, while the other rod is only lightly held in place so that it can be slid in or out to strike the arc. A small wooden dowel is drilled out to accept one end of the movable carbon rod, and the rod is glued into place. The dowel thus serves as a handle to move the one carbon rod in or out. Connections to the carbon rods are made by sheet metal screws attached to the metal clamps.

Fig. 2-15 shows how to wire up the demonstration carbon arc. One lead from the carbon arc assembly goes to one terminal of the cone heater element. The other lead from the cone heater element goes to one end of the line cord.

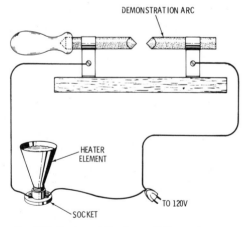

Fig. 2-15. Hookup of the demonstration carbon arc.

Finally, the other end of the line cord is connected to the remaining carbon arc assembly terminal.

To place the demonstration carbon arc into operation, connect the line cord to a source of 120 volts. NOTE: The cone heater element, which serves as a current-limiting resistor, will become quite hot. Take care not to touch it or to allow any flammable material to come into contact with it. Momentarily touch the movable electrode to the stationary carbon electrode, then slowly move the movable electrode away from the stationary electrode. A brilliant arc will develop between the electrodes. A little patience is necessary in order to establish a stable arc.

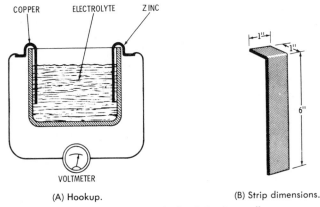

(A) Hookup. (B) Strip dimensions.

Fig. 2-16. A simple chemical voltage cell.

A SIMPLE CELL

The simple electrochemical cell to be described demonstrates the basic principle of how electricity can be obtained by chemical means. This simple cell is known as a *voltaic* cell.

Fig. 2-16 shows the required setup. Select a wide-mouth jar, such as the type that peanut butter or jelly are packed in. Next, cut a strip of copper and a strip of zinc to the dimensions shown in Fig. 2-16B. The copper can be flashing, which is sold in hardware stores. The zinc can be salvaged from an old dry cell. As shown, the tops of the strips are bent at right angles, and wires are soldered to the two strips.

Pour a diluted solution of sulfuric acid (about 10%) into the jar until the jar is about ⅔ full. This sulfuric acid solution can be obtained either from a chemical supply house or from an automotive supply store. (It is used in storage batteries.)

Place the strips of metal into the jar and connect a low-range voltmeter to the wires soldered to the strips. The voltmeter should indicate a voltage of approximately 1.5 volts. If desired, a small light bulb can be connected across the wires from the strips.

When experimenting with this simple cell, you will note bubbles developing around the zinc plate. The number of bubbles produced is greater when current is being drawn from the cell. These bubbles are hydrogen gas liberated from the zinc strip as a result of chemical reaction of the zinc with the sulfuric acid.

A variation of this voltaic cell is the voltaic pile, which consists of a number of individual voltaic cells stacked in series. The advantage of this arrangement is that a higher voltage can be obtained than from a single cell.

Fig. 2-17 shows how to construct a simple voltaic pile. Cut out five zinc discs and five copper discs as shown in Fig. 2-17A. Additionally, cut out five discs from blotting paper. Moisten each blotting paper disc with a strong solution of salt water. Alternately stack copper, zinc, and blotting paper discs. When all discs are stacked, connect a voltmeter across the completed stack as shown in Fig. 2-17B. You will note that a higher voltage is developed across the stack than was obtained across the single voltaic cell.

A DEMONSTRATION STORAGE CELL

The simple voltaic cell is known as a *primary* cell, as are the common flashlight cells. All primary cells have the characteristic that once they have used up their chemical-producing materials, they are dead, and cannot be successfully rejuvenated, except by replacing their chemical contents.

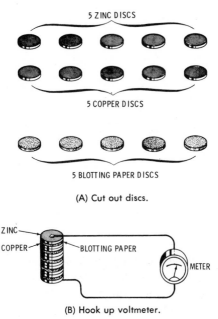

5 ZINC DISCS

5 COPPER DISCS

5 BLOTTING PAPER DISCS

(A) Cut out discs.

ZINC
COPPER
BLOTTING PAPER
METER

(B) Hook up voltmeter.

Fig. 2-17. Demonstration voltaic pile.

On the other hand, a *secondary* cell is capable of having its electrochemical process reversed, so that it may be recharged back to its original current-producing state. Although there are now a number of secondary cells available, such as the *nickel-cadmium* type, the earliest and most common type is the *lead-acid* secondary cell. This is the type of cell that is used in your automobile.

To assemble a demonstration lead-acid secondary cell, you will need a glass jar such as the type peanut butter or jelly is packed in, two strips of sheet lead, and enough diluted sulfuric acid to fill ⅔ jar.

To assemble the demonstration storage cell, bend each of the lead strips at right angles. Solder a short length of hookup wire to each of the lead strips. Next, fill the jar ⅔ full with the diluted sulfuric acid and place the strips into the acid, as shown in Fig. 2-18.

Before the secondary cell can deliver current, it must first be *formed* by passing a current through it. The method for doing this is shown in Fig. 2-19. Connect four No. 6

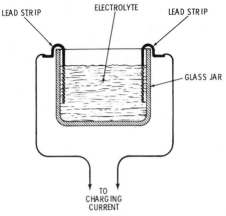

Fig. 2-18. Construction of a demonstration storage cell.

dry cells or a lantern battery in series with a switch and cell plates as shown. Close the switch and allow the current to flow for about five minutes. At this time, you will notice that the plates have changed color, indicating that a chemical change has taken place. Disconnect the dry cells, and connect a low-range voltmeter to the wires that are connected to the lead strips. You will find that approximately

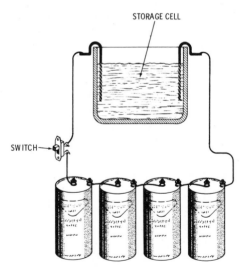

Fig. 2-19. "Forming" the storage cell.

two volts are developed by the cell. You can connect a 1½- or 2-volt light bulb to the leads from the cell. If the bulb is left connected to the cell for any length of time, the cell will slowly discharge, until a point is reached where it will no longer deliver current. The cell is now said to be discharged. To *recharge* the cell, it is only necessary to reform it as was done initially.

3

Experiments With Magnetism

In this chapter, a number of interesting experiments involving magnetism and electromagnetism will be described.

A SIMPLE COMPASS

One of the earliest applications of magnetism was the magnetic compass. The earliest compass was a piece of *lodestone* (iron oxide) suspended by a string, as shown in Fig. 3-1. In operation, the lodestone would swing around so that the same part of it would always point to the north.

Fig. 3-2 shows a very simple magnetic compass. A small bar magnet is placed on top of a cork which, in turn, is placed in a small dish of water. You will notice, after a moment or so, that the cork will swing around so that the bar magnet is aligned with the magnetic poles of the earth. The south pole of the bar magnet will point to the north pole of the earth and vice versa.

LINES OF FORCE AROUND A MAGNET

The attraction power of a magnet is due to the presence of magnetic lines of force produced around the magnet. The greater the number of these lines of force, the greater is the "pull" of the magnet.

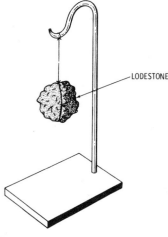

LODESTONE

Fig. 3-1. The earliest compass.

Although these magnetic lines of force are not visible, their presence can be easily demonstrated. Fig. 3-3 shows the setup. As shown, a piece of either glass or clear plastic is supported on two blocks. A quantity of iron filings is spread over the surface of the plate. These iron filings can be obtained from a chemical supply company. Shake the plate so as to evenly distribute the filings over its surface.

Now, take a small bar magnet and place it underneath the plate. You will notice that the iron filings will arrange themselves in a pattern similar to that shown in Fig. 3-4. The iron filings align themselves in a pattern that corresponds to the position of the magnetic lines of force.

Next, take a small horseshoe magnet and place it underneath the plate. You will now obtain a pattern similar to that shown in Fig. 3-5.

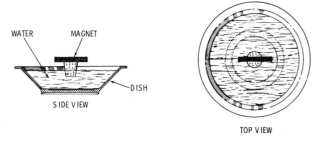

WATER   MAGNET

DISH

SIDE VIEW

TOP VIEW

Fig. 3-2. A simple compass.

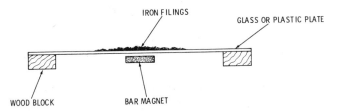

Fig. 3-3. Setup for demonstrating magnetic lines of force.

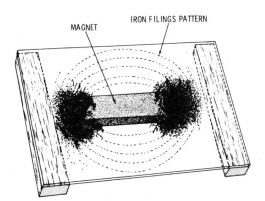

Fig. 3-4. Iron filings show magnetic lines of force.

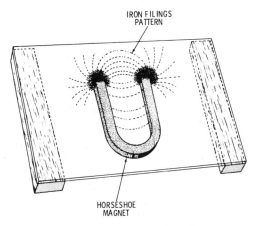

Fig. 3-5. Magnetic field around a bar magnet.

A SIMPLE GALVANOMETER

A galvanometer is a device used to indicate the presence of small electrical currents. Although commercial galvanometers are quite expensive, you can construct a simple, inexpensive galvanometer. Despite its simplicity, this galvanometer is capable of providing surprising sensitivity.

Fig. 3-6 shows how the galvanometer is assembled. A small pocket compass is used as the basic indicator. As shown in Fig. 3-6A, 50 turns of No. 30 enamel magnet wire are wound around the center of the compass. Secure this winding in place with a coating of duco cement or other

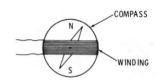

(A) Pocket compass as basic indicator.

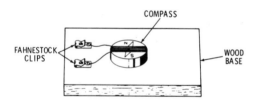

(B) Cement compass on piece of wood.

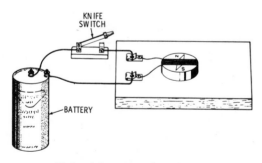

(C) Attach batteries and switch.

Fig. 3-6. A simple galvanometer.

similar cement such as coil dope. Next, cement the compass (and its winding) on a small piece of wood to which two Fahnestock clips have been attached, as shown in Fig. 3-6B. The final step in assembly is to remove the enamel insulation from the ends of the leads from the winding around the compass, and attach them to the Fahnestock clips.

Fig. 3-6C shows how the galvanometer may be used to indicate the presence of current. Connect a lead from one terminal of a 1.5-volt dry cell to one galvanometer Fahnestock clip. Connect another lead from the other galvanometer Fahnestock clip to one terminal of the switch. Finally, connect a lead from the remaining switch terminal to the remaining battery terminal.

To operate the galvanometer, momentarily close the switch. Notice that the compass needle will quickly swing to a position that is at a right angle to the winding, as shown in Fig. 3-7A. Now, reverse the battery terminal connection and again momentarily close the switch. This time, note that the compass needle again swings to a position that is at a right angle to the coil—however, this time the "north" point of the compass needle is reversed, as shown in Fig. 3-7B. Thus, this galvanometer may be used to indicate both the presence and direction of an applied electric current. This little galvanometer will be used in future experiments in this chapter.

PRODUCING AN ELECTRIC CURRENT
BY MEANS OF A MAGNETIC FIELD

Magnetism and electricity are directly interrelated—an electric current can be generated by means of a moving magnetic field, and mechanical motion can be produced when an electric current-carrying conductor is placed in a magnetic field.

Fig. 3-8 shows how an electric current can be produced from a moving electric field. To set up the experiment, first wind a coil of 100 turns of No. 30 enamel magnet wire. Tape the coil turns in place with small pieces of tape.

Next, remove the insulation from the ends of the coil leads, and connect them to the galvanometer Fahnestock

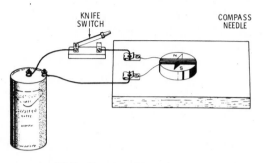

(A) Needle swings in one direction.

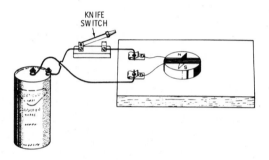

(B) Needle swings in opposite direction.

Fig. 3-7. Galvanometer indicates direction of current.

clips, as in Fig. 3-8. Now, take a bar magnet and rapidly pass it in and out through the center of the coil. As you do this, you will notice that the galvanometer swings around,

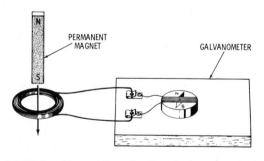

Fig. 3-8. Motion of magnet through coil produces a current in the coil.

first in one direction, then in the other direction. Notice that when the magnet is thrust through the coil in one direction, the galvanometer needle swings in one direction. Reversing the movement of the magnet through the coil will cause the galvanometer needle to swing in the other direction. From these results, we can see that when a magnet moves through a number of conductors (the coil) in one direction, current is produced in one direction. The direction of the current is reversed when the direction of the magnet movement is reversed. You will also notice as the speed of the magnet through the coil is increased, the amount of current generated will also be greater as indicated by a greater swing of the compass needle.

PRODUCING MECHANICAL MOTION
FROM A MAGNETIC FIELD

When current is passed through a conductor (or conductors) placed in a magnetic field, the conductor will move in relation to the magnetic field. This fact can be easily demonstrated by the setup shown in Fig. 3-9. Wind a coil, consisting of 50 turns of No. 20 enamel magnet wire. Remove the insulation from the ends of the coil lead to one terminal of two series-connected dry cells. Leave the other coil lead free for a moment, as shown in Fig. 3-9A. Referring to Fig. 3-9B, slip the coil over a bar magnet that is placed in the upright position. Finally, momentarily touch the remaining coil lead to the remaining battery terminal. The coil will "jump" up into the air.

Now, touch the remaining coil lead to the junction of the two dry cells. This time the coil will not "jump" as high as before, indicating that the amount of mechanical motion is dependent upon the strength of the current through the coil.

AN ELECTROMAGNET

There are two basic types of magnets—the permanent magnet and the electromagnet. The permanent magnet retains its magnetism for an indefinite length of time once it has been initially magnetized. The electromagnet possesses

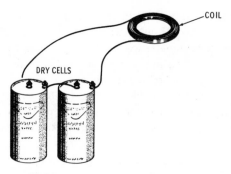

(A) Connect one end of coil to batteries.

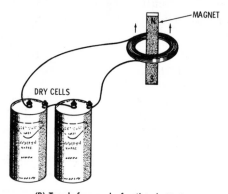

(B) Touch free end of coil to batteries.

Fig. 3-9. Mechanical motion from a magnetic field.

magnetic properties only while it is energized by an electric current through it.

Fig. 3-10 shows how a simple electromagnet can be constructed. As shown in Fig. 3-10A, use a stove bolt, 3 inches long and ¼ inch in diameter and fashion two washers out of stiff cardboard. These washers are slipped over the ends of the stove bolt and secured in place by a bit of duco cement. Wrap a single layer of electrical tape over the bolt. Wind numerous layers of No. 18 enamel magnet wire around the bolt, as shown in Fig. 3-10B. Place the ends of the winding through two holes punched in one of the cardboard washers.

As shown in Fig. 3-10C, remove the insulation from the ends of the coil lead, and connect one of these leads to one

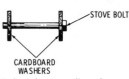

STOVE BOLT

CARDBOARD
WASHERS

(A) Stove bolt and two cardboard
washers.

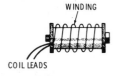

WINDING

COIL LEADS

(B) Wind layers of wire around bolt.

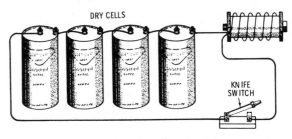

DRY CELLS

KNIFE
SWITCH

(C) Hook up dry cells and switch.

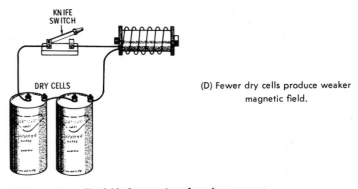

KNIFE
SWITCH

DRY CELLS

(D) Fewer dry cells produce weaker
magnetic field.

Fig. 3-10. Construction of an electromagnet.

terminal of four series-connected No. 6 dry cells. Connect
the other coil terminal to one terminal of a knife switch.
Finally, connect the remaining switch terminal to the remaining battery terminal.

To operate the electromagnet, close the knife switch.
Bring a piece of steel or iron near either end of the electromagnet. The metal will be attracted to the bolt. This will
indicate that a magnetic field has developed around the
magnet.

Open the knife switch and connect the batteries as shown in Fig. 3-10D. Again close the knife switch. You will find that the magnetic field produced by the electromagnet is weaker, due to the lower applied voltage.

Again, close the knife switch and bring a compass near one end of the electromagnet, as shown in Fig. 3-11A. Note which way the compass needle is deflected. Now, reverse the battery connections as shown in Fig. 3-11B. This time, the compass needle will swing around in the opposite direction. This indicates that the magnetic poles (north and south) of the electromagnet are reversed when the voltage applied to the electromagnet is reversed.

Fig. 3-12 shows a variation of the simple electromagnet. Two stove bolts are wound full of No. 18 enamel magnet wire. The ends of the bolts are mounted to a steel bracket

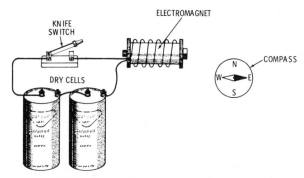

(A) Compass needle swings in one direction.

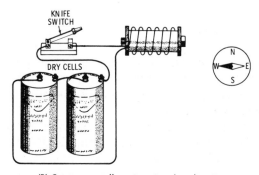

(B) Compass needle swings in other direction.

Fig. 3-11. Effect of an electromagnet on a compass.

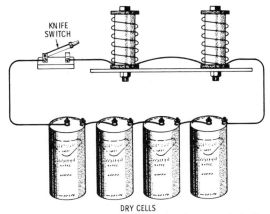

KNIFE SWITCH

DRY CELLS

Fig. 3-12. Two electromagnets increase the magnetic field.

as shown. When connected to four series-connected No. 6 cells, a fairly powerful electromagnet will be obtained. This additional magnetic strength is due to the concentration of the magnetic fields of the two electromagnets at the "open" ends of the two stove bolts.

NOTE: Due to the relatively high current drawn by both of the previously described electromagnets, they should not be left connected to the battery for more than about 30 seconds at a time.

MAGNETIC SOLENOID

One of the many practical applications of the electromagnet is the solenoid. Fig. 3-13 shows how a simple magnetic solenoid may be constructed.

Make up a cardboard tube by rolling up a piece of cardboard, as shown in Fig. 3-13A. The tube should have an inside diameter of approximately ⅜ inch and a length of 4 inches. Make two cardboard washers as shown and slip one washer over each end of the finished tube. Secure these washers in place with a bit of duco cement.

Next, wind this prepared coil form full of No. 18 enamel magnet wire. Pass the ends of the finished winding out through two small holes in one washer, as shown in Fig. 3-13B.

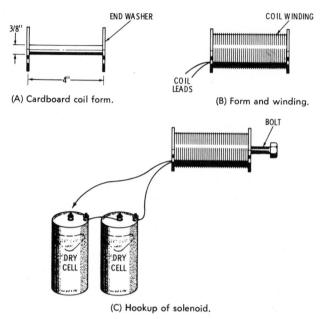

(A) Cardboard coil form.

(B) Form and winding.

(C) Hookup of solenoid.

Fig. 3-13. Construction of a simple solenoid.

Referring to Fig. 3-13C, insert a ⅜- by 2-inch stove bolt partially into the finished solenoid coil. Connect one lead from the solenoid coil to one terminal of two series-connected No. 6 dry cells. Momentarily touch the remaining solenoid coil lead to the remaining battery terminal. The stove bolt will be rapidly "sucked" into the solenoid.

A MAGNETIC SOLENOID DICE THROWER

Fig. 3-14 shows a novel application of the solenoid. As shown in Fig. 3-14A, the solenoid coil just described is mounted on a small wooden board so its bottom end is approximately ½ inch above the top of the board. A pushbutton switch (momentary-contact) is screwed to the board and a ⅜- by 4½-inch machine bolt is inserted into the solenoid coil from the bottom (Fig. 3-14B). The bolt will have to be placed into the coil before the coil is mounted into place. One lead from the coil is connected to one terminal of the pushbutton switch; the other switch terminal is con-

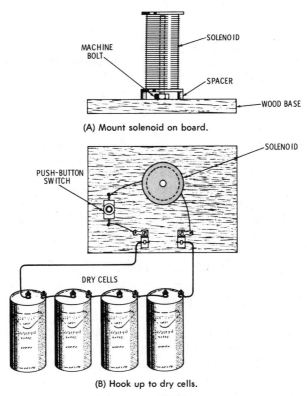

(A) Mount solenoid on board.

(B) Hook up to dry cells.

Fig. 3-14. Magnetic dice thrower.

nected to one terminal of four series-connected No. 6 dry cells. Finally, the remaining solenoid coil terminal is attached to the remaining battery terminal.

In operation, two dice are stacked on top of the opening in the solenoid coil and the pushbutton is depressed. The stove bolt will be quickly drawn up into the solenoid, kicking the dice high up into the air.

MAGNETIC SORTER

Here is a novel application of magnetism. Mix together a small quantity of iron and brass filings, and pour them out on a small piece of cardboard as shown in Fig. 3-15A. Slowly pass a small permanent magnet across the filing mixture as

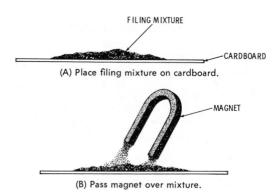

(A) Place filing mixture on cardboard.

(B) Pass magnet over mixture.

Fig. 3-15 A simple magnetic sorter.

shown in Fig. 3-15B. The iron filings will be attracted to the magnet while the nonmagnetic brass filings will remain behind.

Fig. 3-16 shows another approach to the magnetic separator (sorter) idea. Here, the mixture of magnetic and nonmagnetic material is passed down a small diameter paper or plastic tube. A magnet is placed against the outside of the tube. As the particle mixture passes down through the tube, the magnetic particles will be attracted and hold to the sides of the tube, while the nonmagnetic particles pass on down through the tube. This method of material separation is widely used in industrial processes.

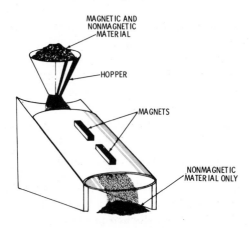

Fig. 3-16. Magnetic separator.

THE BOUNCING SPRING

This is a very interesting demonstration of electromagnetic attraction in a wire carrying an electric current. Fig. 3-17A shows the basic setup. Begin by drilling a 1-inch hole into, but not through, a block of wood. (Plastic may be

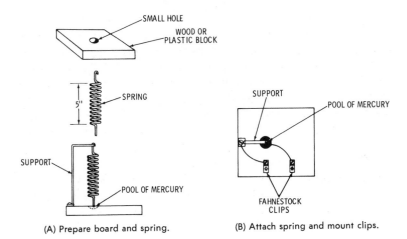

(A) Prepare board and spring.   (B) Attach spring and mount clips.

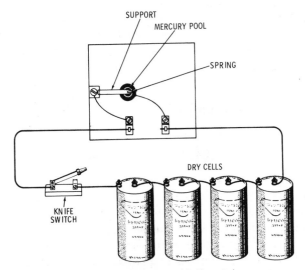

(C) Hook up batteries and knife switch.

Fig. 3-17. A bouncing spring.

used if desired.) Next, wind a long spring out of No. 14 enamel magnet wire, as shown in Fig. 3-17B. Fasten one end of the spring to an upright support made from a piece of stiff wire such as from a coat hanger, which is attached to the wooden base. Run a lead from the top of the spring where it is connected to the support down to a Fahnestock clip. Position a piece of stiff bus wire so that it fits down into the hole in the block. Connect a lead from this stiff wire to a second Fahnestock clip. Pour a small amount of mercury into the hole. The amount of mercury should be to the point where it just covers the tip of the spring. Finally, as shown in Fig. 3-17C, connect a lead from one Fahnestock clip to one terminal of four series-connected No. 6 dry cells. Connect a lead from the other Fahnestock clip to one terminal of a knife switch. Finally, connect a lead from the remaining switch terminal to the remaining battery terminal.

To place the bouncing spring into operation, close the knife switch. The path of the current is from the battery into the mercury pool, up through the spring, through the closed switch, and back into the battery. Here is how the bouncing spring works: When current initially enters into the spring, a magnetic field is built up around its turns. This magnetic field causes attraction between adjacent turns of the spring, and it contracts. As the spring contracts, the free end no longer contacts the pool of mercury which interrupts the current through the spring. The spring now "relaxes" and its end again contacts the mercury, and the whole process starts all over, causing the spring to bounce up and down.

INDUCTION-LOOP TRANSMITTER

This induction-loop transmitter is a very novel way to demonstrate electromagnetic induction. Fig. 3-18A shows the basic setup for the induction-loop transmitter. Wind two large coils (12 inches in diameter) with No. 22 enamel magnet wire. A handy way to wind these coils is to drive a series of small nails in a wooden board in a ring shape, as shown in Fig. 3-18B. Wind the wire across the outside of this "ring." Each coil should consist of about 50 turns.

(A) Wind two large coils.

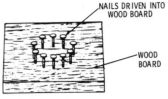

NAILS DRIVEN INTO
WOOD BOARD

WOOD
BOARD

(B) Use nail board to wind coils.

Fig. 3-18. Basic setup for induction-loop transmitter.

When the two coils are finished, tape the wire in place with small pieces of tape. Finally, remove the insulation from the ends of the coil windings.

Fig. 3-19 shows how the induction-loop transmitter is hooked up. The "transmitting" loop is connected in series with a carbon mike, a switch, and four series-connected No. 6 dry cells.

The receiving loop is connected to a pair of 2000-ohm headphones. To operate the induction-loop transmitter, place the "transmitter" and "receiver" loops in a parallel plane, and about a foot apart. Close the switch and speak into the microphone. The speech should be clearly audible in the phones. Now, move the loops farther apart and note that the loops can be separated a fairly good distance and still obtain satisfactory results. Remember, for best results, these two loops must be kept in a parallel plane.

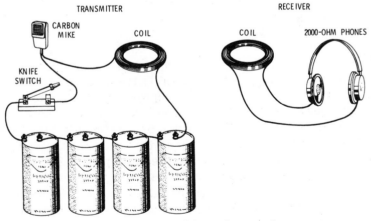

Fig. 3-19. The hookup of the wireless transmitter.

Fig. 3-20 shows how the output of the receiver loop can be amplified. An Allied Radio Part No. 24-A-9466 solid-state audio amplifier module is connected to the output of the "receiving" loop to boost the signal picked up by this loop.

GROUND TELEPHONE

This ground telephone demonstrates a novel method of communication, which takes advantage of the electrical conductivity of the crust of the earth.

The basic ground telephone setup is shown in Fig. 3-21A. Start by driving two copper rods into the earth, to a depth of over 1 foot. The rods should be spaced at least 12 feet apart. Attach a length of hookup wire to each of these "ground rods." Connect the length of hookup wire attached to one of the ground rods to one terminal of a knife switch. Connect the other terminal of the switch to one terminal

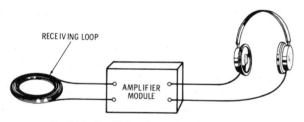

Fig. 3-20. Amplifying the receiver loop output.

of four series-connected No. 6 dry cells. Connect the remaining terminal of the battery to one terminal of a carbon microphone. Connect the other terminal of the microphone to the hookup wire attached to the other ground rod.

For the "receiver," drive two copper rods into the earth, as in the case of the "transmitter" rods. Again, the rods should be at least 12 feet apart. For best results, the "receiving" rods should be in line with the "transmitting" rods. Lengths of hookup wire are attached to a pair of 2000-ohm headphones, as shown in Fig. 3-21B.

To operate the "ground telephone," close the knife switch and speak into the carbon microphone. Your voice should come through clearly in the headphones.

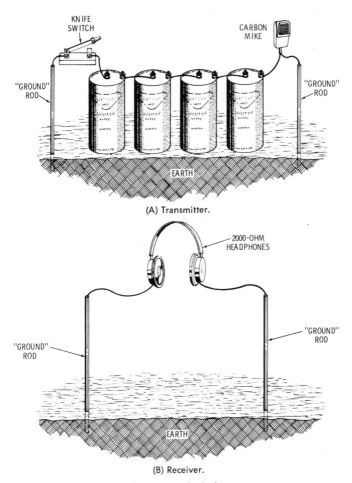

(A) Transmitter.

(B) Receiver.

Fig. 3-21. Basic ground telephone setup.

Experimenting with the "ground telephone" will yield some interesting results. For example, a greater range will be obtained if the transmitting rods are placed farther apart. Also, as the distance between the transmitting and receiving rods is increased, the signal level will decrease, and vice versa.

The amount of moisture in the earth surrounding the transmitting and receiving rods will have a great effect on the operating range of this system. The greater the mois-

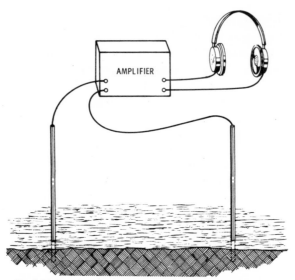

Fig. 3-22. Boosting the receiver output with a transistor amplifier.

ture, the greater the operating range. If the ground is very dry, try spraying the area between the transmitting and receiving rods with a solution of salt water. This will considerably reduce the resistance of the earth.

Another method of increasing the operating range of the ground telephone is to connect a miniature transistor amplifier, such as a Lafayette No. 99-E-90383, between the receiving wires and headphones, as shown in Fig. 3-22.

SOUND-POWERED TELEPHONE

This novel telephone system requires no external source of operating power, such as batteries, etc. Fig. 3-23 shows

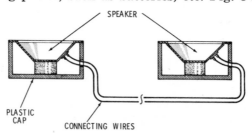

Fig. 3-23. Simple sound-powered phones.

the sound-powered telephone setup. Two miniature 2¼-inch loudspeakers are mounted in small plastic cups. Suitable cups may be obtained from aerosol can tops. Before mounting the speaker, solder the ends from a length of two-conductor lamp cord to the terminals of the two speakers. The lamp cord can be passed through holes drilled in the plastic cups. The length of the cord between speakers can be up to 100 feet or so. Due to the low impedance of the speakers, it is not necessary to use shielded wire. The speaker is secured in place by cementing the rim to the cup edge with a bit of duco cement.

To use the sound-powered phone, simply talk into either speaker. Sound waves generated by your voice cause the "microphone" speaker cone to vibrate. In turn, this generates a small current that is fed along the lamp cord to the "receiver" speaker. This current causes the "receiver" speaker cone to vibrate in step with the original speech sounds.

MAGNETIC SHAKE TABLE

This novel gadget is a miniature version of the shake table used in industry. As shown in Fig. 3-24, our miniature shake table consists of an 8-inch loudspeaker mounted horizontally on a small board. A handy method of mounting the speaker is to apply a bit of epoxy cement to the base of the speaker frame and then set the speaker on the mounting board. Allow at least 24 hours for the epoxy to dry.

The speaker cone should be stiffened by applying at least three coats of "radio service" cement to it. A stiff piece of cardboard, which serves as a platform for holding the items

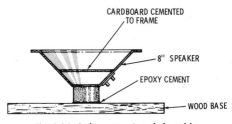

Fig. 3-24. A demonstration shake table.

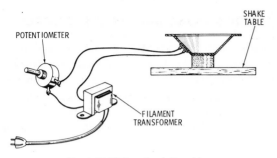

Fig. 3-25. Wiring the shake table.

to be vibrated, is cemented on the cone as shown in Fig. 3-24.

Fig. 3-25 shows how the shake table speaker is hooked up. The potentiometer should be at least a 2.5-ohm unit. The filament transformer should have a secondary current rating of at least ½ ampere.

To operate the shake table, place the material to be shaken on the speaker platform. NOTE: The material placed on the platform should not weigh more than a few ounces; otherwise, the speaker cone will "bottom." With the filament transformer connected to a 120Vac source, adjust the potentiometer for the desired speaker-cone movement.

Fig. 3-26 shows a variation of the above approach. Here, the shaker speaker is connected to the output of an audio amplifier, the input of which is fed from an audio-frequency oscillator. By using this approach, the frequency applied to the shaker speaker can be varied to find the optimum shaker frequency. Also, the effect of various vibrating frequencies on different substances can be observed.

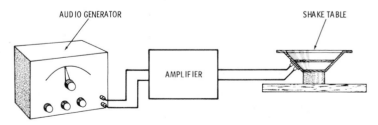

Fig. 3-26. Using an audio generator with the shake table.

VARIABLE-REACTANCE POWER CONTROL

This gadget can find a number of practical applications around the home, lab, or shop. For example, it can be used as a light dimmer, or to control the temperature of your soldering iron. Unlike a rheostat, this variable-reactance control uses no power in the form of heat.

Fig. 3-27 shows how the variable-reactance power control is constructed. Start by making up a coil form from cardboard, as shown in Fig. 3-27A. Apply several coats of radio service cement to the finished coil form to strengthen it. Next, cut two cardboard washers, and slip one of them over each end of the tube as shown. Secure these washers in place with a bit of radio service cement or duco cement.

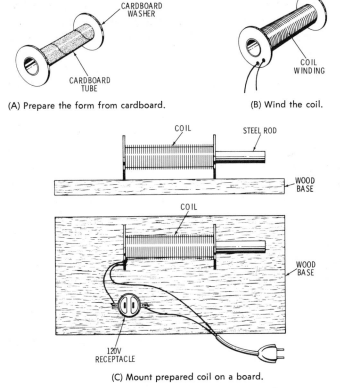

(A) Prepare the form from cardboard.

(B) Wind the coil.

(C) Mount prepared coil on a board.

Fig. 3-27. Variable-reactance power control.

Wind the coil form full of No. 16 enamel magnet wire. Pass the ends of the completed winding through two small holes drilled (or punched) in one of the end washers on the form, as shown in Fig. 3-27B.

Mount the prepared coil on a wooden board, along with a 120-volt receptacle, as shown in Fig. 3-27C. The movable core consists of a ½-inch steel rod, 3 inches long. This bar, which controls the effective reactance of the coil, should slide easily in and out of the coil core.

To operate the variable-reactance power control, plug the device to be controlled—light, soldering iron, etc.—into the 120-volt receptable, and plug the power-control line cord into a 120Vac source. With the steel bar all the way out of the coil, nearly 120 volts will be applied to the controlled device. As the steel core is slid into the coil, the reactance of the coil increases and the voltage applied to the load decreases. Minimum voltage is applied to the load when the core is all the way into the coil. The maximum current-carrying capacity of the power controller is about 500 watts.

A MAGNETIC STIRRER

Fig. 3-28 shows the basic idea of the magnetic stirrer. A bar magnet is attached to the shaft of a small motor. The drive motor and its spinning magnet are mounted beneath a platform on which the container in which the liquid to be stirred is placed. A second bar magnet is placed in the container along with the liquid to be stirred.

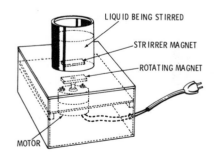

LIQUID BEING STIRRED

STIRRER MAGNET

ROTATING MAGNET

MOTOR

Fig. 3-28. Operation of a magnetic stirrer.

In operation, the spinning magnet attached to the motor shaft "pulls around" the second bar magnet immersed in the liquid in the container by virtue of magnetic attraction. The bar magnet that is immersed in the liquid is generally coated with an inert material, such as a Teflon coating, so that it will not be attacked by a possibly corrosive solution that may be placed in the container.

Fig. 3-29 shows the construction details of a simple magnetic stirrer that you can build. The motor is of the "universal" type, that is, it contains a wound armature and brushes, and will then operate on either ac or dc. This type of motor is required so that it can be used with a variable speed control.

As shown in Fig. 3-29A, a shaft coupler is attached to the shaft of the motor. The magnet is connected to the end of the shaft coupler. Since a metal-to-metal bond is required, it is best to use a good grade of epoxy cement for the gluing job.

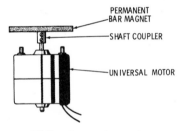

(A) Mount magnet on motor.

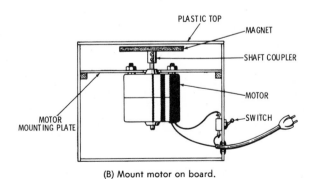

(B) Mount motor on board.

Fig. 3-29. Construction of magnetic stirrer.

The motor is mounted in a vertical position on the bottom of a homemade wooden enclosure, as shown in Fig. 3-29B. No dimensions are given for the enclosure, since they will depend upon the type of motor that you select. The magnets selected should have good strength for reliable operation.

The platform on which the mixing container is placed should be fairly thin to allow the "drive" and "stirrer" magnets to be in close proximity to each other. A good solution might be a piece of No. 18 or No. 20 gauge aluminum sheet or plastic. Needless to say, iron or steel cannot be used here, because such materials would block the magnetic field from the "drive" magnet. By the same token, any container used to hold the solution being mixed must be made from a nonferrous material.

Finishing touches to the stirrer include attaching a line cord and a switch, as shown in the sketch of the completed unit.

To obtain best results from the magnetic stirrer, it is highly recommended that some sort of motor speed control be used. This can be either a variable transformer or an SCR speed control, the latter being less expensive.

MAGNETIZER

This is a handy gadget for the quick magnetizing or the restoration of magnetism to permanent magnets. Unlike the more familiar method of magnetizing an object where a magnet is rubbed against the material to be magnetized, this device applies an instantaneous, high magnetic field over the entire area of the object to be magnetized. Actually, this magnetizer is a miniature version of the commercial impulse magnetizers.

Fig. 3-30 is the schematic of the magnetizer. In operation, when switch S1 is closed, 120 volts ac is applied to the primary of power transformer T1. The voltage appearing across the secondary is rectified by diode D1. Now, assume that switch S2 is placed in position 1. Capacitors C1, C2, and C3 will slowly charge up to the peak dc voltage developed from diode D1. When this point is reached, NE-2 will light, signalling that the capacitors are fully charged.

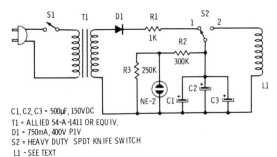

C1, C2, C3 = 500μF, 150VDC
T1 = ALLIED 54-A-1411 OR EQUIV.
D1 = 750mA, 400V PIV
S2 = HEAVY DUTY SPDT KNIFE SWITCH
L1 - SEE TEXT

Fig. 3-30. Schematic diagram of a magnetizer.

Now, assume that switch S2 is thrown to position 2. The fully charged capacitors will very quickly discharge through coil L1, thus generating a large magnetic field around it. This large, momentary magnetic field effectively magnetizes the item placed within the coil.

Fig. 3-31 is a pictorial diagram of the magnetizer. Parts layout is not particularly critical, although there are several points that must be kept in mind. You will note that switch S2 is a heavy-duty knife switch, rather than the more conventional toggle switch. The reason for this is that the discharge current of the capacitors is very high; thus, the contacts of a smaller switch would just weld together. Due to the large current through L1 when C1 is discharged, it is a free-standing coil of 8 turns of No. 12 enamel magnet wire wound 3 inches in diameter.

To operate the magnetizer, simply place the object to be magnetized in the center of L1. Apply power and place switch S2 in position 1. After a few moments, the neon

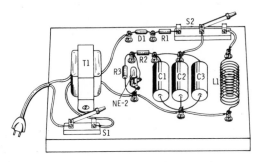

Fig. 3-31. Pictorial diagram of a magnetizer.

lamp will light, indicating that the capacitors are fully charged. Now, throw S2 to position 2. You will hear a loud "crack" as the capacitors discharge through L1. The object placed within L1 will now be magnetized.

DEMAGNETIZER

The project is designed to do just the opposite of the last gadget, mainly demagnetize an object. This demagnetizer is handy for such applications as demagnetizing screwdrivers, watches, and magnetic recording tape.

Fig. 3-32 shows the construction details of the demagnetizer. To start off, use an old choke either from your junk box or from an old radio, amplifier, or TV set. Remove the winding from the choke by sawing through it with a hacksaw or unwind it if you wish to salvage the wire. The choke that you select must have a core area at least as large as, or larger than, that shown in Fig. 3-32A.

After you have removed the winding(s) from the core, the next step is to separate the core stack into E and I sections. The easiest way of doing this is shown in Fig. 3-32B. Take a sharp screwdriver or chisel, and place the blade at the point on the core where the E and I sections meet. A

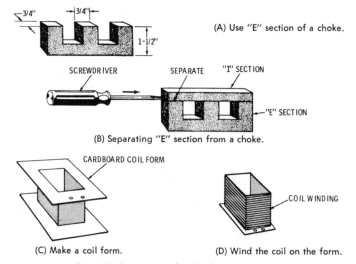

(A) Use "E" section of a choke.

(B) Separating "E" section from a choke.

(C) Make a coil form.

(D) Wind the coil on the form.

Fig. 3-32. Construction details of a demagnetizer.

good crack on the handle of the screwdriver or chisel with a hammer will readily separate the E and I sections.

The next step is to make a coil form for the demagnetizer winding. Take a piece of stiff cardboard and bend it around the center leg of the E section, as shown in Fig. 3-32C. Tape the ends of the cardboard in place and remove it from the core. Apply several coats of radio service cement or duco cement to the cardboard to stiffen it. Make two end washers for the cardboard coil form to hold the winding in place. These washers can be held in place with radio service cement or duco cement.

The next step is to prepare the winding. Obtain a 1-lb. spool of No. 18 enamel magnet wire. Pass one end of the wire through a small hole punched in one of the cardboard washers, and begin winding the coil. Lay the winding down in neat layers and avoid any overlapping of the winding. Continue the winding to a depth where the wire is about even with the cardboard washers, as shown in Fig. 3-32D. Cut the wire at this point, and pass the end of the wire through a hole punched in the cardboard washer. The coil winding is now complete, and it should be covered with a layer of electrical tape for protection. Place the finished coil over the center leg of the E section.

Now, mount the assembled coil/core on a wooden base by means of small angle brackets as shown in Fig. 3-33. Mount an spst toggle switch on the board. Wire the toggle switch, coil, and line cord as shown.

To operate the demagnetizer, plug its line cord into a 120 Vac source. NOTE: Do not operate the demagnetizer on

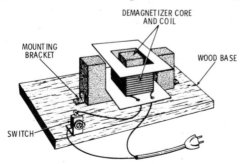

Fig. 3-33. Mounting and wiring the demagnetizer.

direct current, because it will draw excessive current. Place the toggle switch in the ON position, and place the object to be demagnetized in contact with the demagnetizer core. Now, slowly remove the object from the core and move it to a distance of about one foot from the core, and shut off the power to the demagnetizer. That is all there is to it. If the object being demagnetized was highly magnetized, it may be necessary to repeat the demagnetizing procedure several times.

THE SPARK COIL

One of the most fascinating pieces of experimental electrical equipment is the spark coil. A number of fascinating experiments can be performed with the spark coil and a few simple accessories.

Fig. 3-34 shows the basic idea of the spark coil. The basic spark coil is actually a transformer, consisting of a primary and secondary winding wound over a soft-iron core. The primary consists of a relatively few turns of heavy wire, while the secondary contains many turns of very fine wire.

An "interrupter" is connected in series with the primary winding to interrupt at a regular rate the current in the primary. The effect of this interruption is to provide a pulsating current in the primary winding of the spark coil. If the current in the primary were steady, no high voltage would be induced in the secondary winding. The spark coil is generally powered from six volts.

The pulsating current in the primary winding induces a very high voltage across the ends of the secondary winding; this voltage is 10,000 volts or more.

While the spark coil can be found in common use in our automobile as the source of firing voltage for its engine

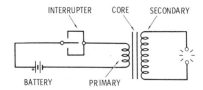

Fig. 3-34. Basic idea of a spark coil.

spark plugs, this type of spark coil is not too well suited for experimental work. The most satisfactory spark coil for experimental work is the Model "T" Ford spark coil, which has an integral interrupter. This is not the case with the modern dry-spark coils that use the engine breaker points to interrupt the current in the coil.

Finding a Model "T" Spark Coil

The Model "T" Ford spark coils can still be located without too much difficulty. One good source of supply is your neighborhood junkyard. There is especially good hunting in rural areas.

If you have no success in your local junkyard, you can purchase a new Model "T" Ford spark coil from the Montgomery-Ward Company, since they still market this item. It is not listed in their general catalog, but they will send you one if you write their main office in Chicago, explaining just what you want. The price of the coil is approximately $6.50.

The coil is supplied with flat terminals as shown in Fig. 3-35. Originally, contact was made to each flat terminal by means of a spring. To modify the coil for experimentation, it is necessary to solder terminals to each of the flat contacts. The approach used by the author was to solder flat-head 8/32 machine screws to the flat terminals. Nuts are then added to serve as binding posts. This is shown in Fig. 3-36.

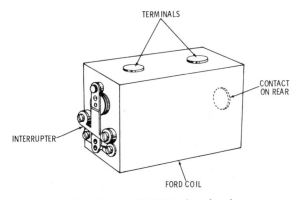

Fig. 3-35. A Model "T" Ford spark coil.

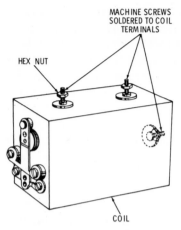

MACHINE SCREWS
SOLDERED TO COIL
TERMINALS

HEX NUT

COIL

Fig. 3-36. Attaching screw terminals
to the coil.

Fig. 3-37 shows how the coil is hooked up. Operating power is obtained either from four series-connected No. 6 dry cells or from a lantern or "hot shot" battery. A spdt switch is included to control the power applied to the coil.

Experiments With the Spark Coil

It is proper to mention that all experiments should be conducted with care. The voltage developed across the secondary terminals of the spark coil is in the neighborhood of 15,000

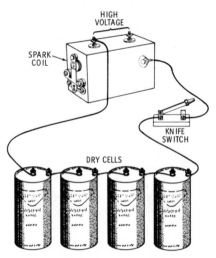

HIGH
VOLTAGE

SPARK
COIL

KNIFE
SWITCH

DRY CELLS

Fig. 3-37. Hookup of the spark coil.

volts. While the current is slight, nevertheless, a dangerous shock will result if contact is made with the secondary terminals of the coil when operating power is applied. Therefore, make sure that the power is removed from the coil before making any contact with the terminals.

Generating a Spark Discharge—Fig. 3-38 shows how the spark coil is used to generate a spark discharge. Connect two lengths of No. 14 bare wire to the secondary terminals of the spark coil. Leave a gap of about ⅛ inch between the ends of the wires. Switch on the power and you will see a bright spark discharge between the ends of the wires. Now, widen the gap and again apply power. You will notice as the gap is widened, the spark discharge becomes thinner and not as bright. Finally, as the gap is increased further, a point will be reached where no spark discharge will take place.

Fig. 3-39 shows a novel way to increase the effective length of the spark discharge. Two insulated wires are run to a glass or plastic plate, and their ends are taped in place. A number of short lengths of bare wire are placed between the ends of the two insulated wires. A ⅛-inch gap is made among the individual smaller wires as shown. When power

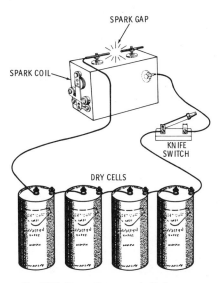

Fig. 3-38. Generating a spark discharge.

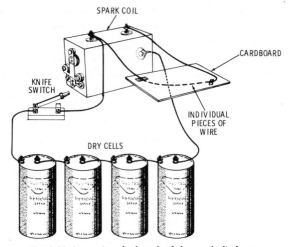

Fig. 3-39. Increasing the length of the spark discharge.

is applied to the spark coil, multiple sparks will jump between the individual small pieces of wire.

Perforating a Cigarette—If you have a friend who smokes cigarettes, try this little trick. Take a cigarette and place it between two wires connected to the secondary terminals, as shown in Fig. 3-40. Apply power to the spark coil, and the

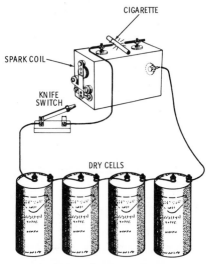

Fig. 3-40. Perforating a cigarette.

spark discharge will produce minute, almost invisible "pin holes" through the cigarettes. When your friend tries to smoke this prepared cigarette, he will not be able to "get a drag" due to the draft through the pin holes.

Jacob's Ladder—This experiment is very fascinating, and is a real conversational piece. It was first demonstrated over a century ago. Fig. 3-41 shows the setup for demonstrating

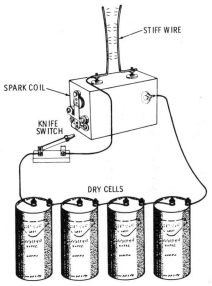

Fig. 3-41. Jacob's ladder demonstration.

the Jacob's ladder. As shown, two No. 14 bare copper wires are attached to the secondary winding binding posts on the spark coil. These two wires are so positioned that they taper slightly apart at the tip.

To set the Jacob's ladder into operation, switch on the power to the spark coil. Sparks will start at the bottom of the wires, bridging the two wires. The sparks will slowly move up the wires until they reach the top, at which point they will disappear, only to reappear at the bottom. This whole process then repeats itself. The sparks' rise up the wires is due to thermal air current.

Discharge in Light Bulb—Fig. 3-42 shows another interesting experiment with the spark coil. Obtain a 100- or 200-

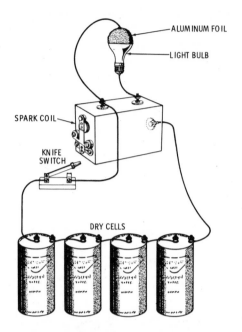

Fig. 3-42. Discharge within light bulb.

watt clear incandescent light bulb. Use duco or radio service cement to secure aluminum foil over the upper portion of the light bulb. Connect a length of insulated wire from the foil to one secondary terminal of the spark coil. Connect a second wire from the base of the bulb to the other secondary terminal of the spark coil.

Apply operating power to the spark coil, and you will observe brilliant streamers emanating from all parts of the wire supports and filaments inside the bulb. It is really a beautiful display. This brilliant color is due to the mixture of gases within the bulb.

Lighting a Fluorescent Tube—Fig. 3-43 shows another novel experiment with the spark coil. As shown, connect the ends of a fluorescent tube to the high voltage secondary terminals of the spark coil. The fluorescent tube can even be burned out. When you switch on the power to the spark coil, the fluorescent tube will light brightly. The reason for this is that the high voltage developed across the secondary

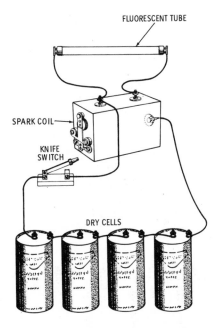

FLUORESCENT TUBE

SPARK COIL

KNIFE SWITCH

DRY CELLS

Fig. 3-43. Lighting of fluorescent tube.

of the spark coil is sufficient to ionize the mercury vapor within the tube.

Fattening the Discharge—Another interesting experiment with the spark coil is shown in Fig. 3-44. Make up a high voltage capacitor as follows. Obtain a piece of window glass at least ⅛-inch thick by 8 inches square. Cut two pieces of aluminum foil, 7 inches square, and cement a piece of foil on each side of the glass as shown. Attach a lead to each of the foils. Attach one lead from the foil to one secondary terminal of the spark coil, and the other foil lead to the remaining secondary lead of the spark coil.

Apply power to the spark coil, and note that the character of the spark discharge has changed considerably. Now, it is heavier or "fatter."

A Demonstration Hertz Transmitter—Heinrich Hertz, a German physicist, used a spark coil transmitter in conjunction with a circular receiver in his early experiments with wireless communication. By use of the spark coil, which we

(A) Capacitor construction.

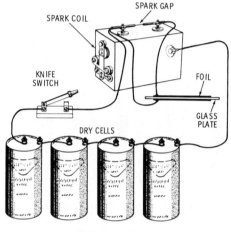

(B) Capacitor hookup.

Fig. 3-44. Adding a capacitor to the spark coil.

have been experimenting with, we can duplicate these early experiments.

As shown in Fig. 3-45, use two wires to make a ⅛-inch spark gap. The ends of these wires should extend out beyond the high voltage secondary terminals for at least one yard. Across the secondary terminals, connect the capacitor described earlier.

The receiver consists of a circular loop of wire, about one foot in diameter. Small metal balls are placed over the ends of the loop, as shown in Fig. 3-46. The spacing between the balls should be about 1/16 inch.

To operate the system, apply power to the spark coil, and bring the receiver loop near the transmitter spark gap. If you look closely, you will see tiny sparks jumping across the balls on the receiver loop.

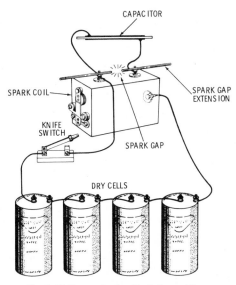

Fig. 3-45. Demonstration Hertz transmitter.

The operation of this system is based upon the fact that the spark discharge creates electromagnetic waves (radio waves), which radiate out from the ends of the spark gap wires. These electromagnetic waves are picked up by the receiving loop, where they induce enough voltage to jump the spark gap between the two balls.

DANCING POLYWOGS

This little project is a real amuser, and can provide hours of entertainment for the younger set. Purchase about a dozen empty gelatin capsules (the kind used to package medicine) from your local druggist. Open the capsule, insert

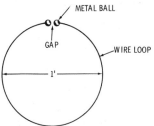

Fig. 3-46. Demonstration Hertz receiver.

CAPSULE
BALL BEARING

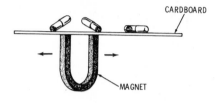

CARDBOARD

Fig. 3-47. Dancing polywogs.

MAGNET

a small ball bearing, as shown in Fig. 3-47, and close the capsule.

Place the capsules with the ball bearings in them on a piece of stiff cardboard, and move a magnet around underneath the cardboard. The capsule will move around, rolling end over end.

A MAGNETIC METAL FINDER

This little gadget is handy for locating several magnetic materials such as small studs, large nails, metal pipes, etc. Simplicity is uppermost; in fact, it would be difficult to find a much simpler metal locator.

As shown in Fig. 3-48, the metal finder consists of a small permanent magnet suspended by a length of thread. The magnet and thread, in turn, are mounted in a small plastic box.

To use the metal finder, hold the plastic box against the wall or other vertical surface where the metal is suspected.

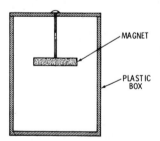

MAGNET

PLASTIC
BOX

Fig. 3-48. A simple metal locater.

When the box is brought near metal, the magnet within it will swing over toward the metal. The sensitivity of the metal finder will be determined by the strength of the magnet.

A NOVEL SYNCHRONOUS MOTOR

This novel motor effectively illustrates the operation of the ac synchronous motor. As shown in Fig. 3-49A, use two steel machine screws, ¼-inch in diameter, and 3 inches long. Make four cardboard washers 1 inch in diameter, with the inside holes just large enough to slip over the ends of the two machine screws as shown.

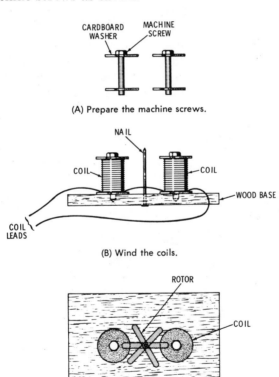

(A) Prepare the machine screws.

(B) Wind the coils.

(C) Construct the rotor.

Fig. 3-49. A demonstration synchronous motor.

Wind each of the screws with 100 turns of No. 18 enamel magnet wire. Pass the beginning and end of each winding through small holes made in the cardboard washers. Wrap the completed windings with a layer of electrical tape.

Mount the two machine screws on a small wooden base, as shown in Fig. 3-49B. A suggested method of mounting the machine screws is to drill two holes in the wooden base just large enough to allow a "force fit" for the screw. If desired, a bit of service cement can be used to further secure the screw in place.

Drill a hole on the wooden base exactly at the center between the two machine screws. Pass a nail through this hole. The tip of the nail should be just slightly higher than the top of the machine screws.

Now, make up a six-sided "rotor" as shown in Fig. 3-49C. (The metal top of a coffee can may be utilized for this purpose.) Using a center punch, make a "dimple" in the center of the rotor. This dimple serves as a bearing. The rotor should spin freely when placed on the nail and given a "flick" with a finger.

The next step is wiring of the motor. Referring to Fig. 3-50, connect one end of the series-connected coils to one

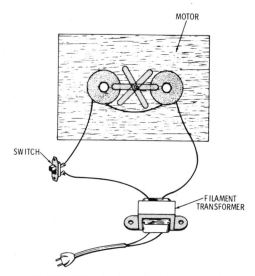

Fig. 3-50. Wiring hookup of synchronous motor.

lead of a 6.3-volt, 2-ampere filament transformer. Connect the remaining lead from the series-connected coils to the terminal of an spst toggle switch. Finally, connect the remaining switch terminal to the remaining filament transformer secondary lead.

To operate the motor, connect the primary of the filament transformer to a 120Vac source, and place the switch in the ON position. Next, spin the rotor briskly with the tip of your finger. When the speed of the rotor is high enough, it will continue to spin.

The synchronous motor is so named because its rate of speed is synchronized with the 60-hertz current alternations applied to its coils from the power line.

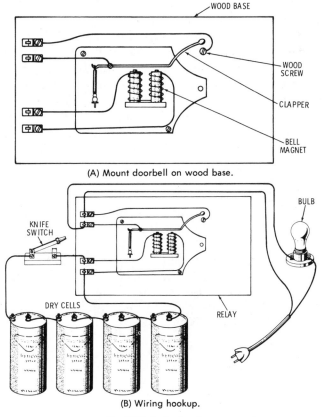

(A) Mount doorbell on wood base.

(B) Wiring hookup.

Fig. 3-51. A simple relay.

A SIMPLE RELAY

This simple relay serves to demonstrate the principle of the electromagnetic relay. As shown in Fig. 3-51A, the basic part of the relay is a doorbell. The first step is to remove the gong portion of the bell, leaving only the clapper, the bar electromagnet, and the contacts. Next, mount the bell on a piece of wood by means of two wood screws. Also, mount a wood screw in such a position that when the clapper is attracted by the magnets, the clapper will touch the screw. Also, on this board, mount four Fahnestock clips by means of wood screws.

As shown, run a wire from each of the Fahnestock clips to each end of the magnet. It will be necessary to remove one end of the magnet winding from the fixed contact, and reconnect it to the Fahnestock clip as shown.

To operate the relay, connect a 120-volt light bulb in series with the relay screw "contacts" and line cord, as shown in Fig. 3-51B. Next, connect a 6-volt battery and a spst switch to the relay coil terminals as shown. Now, close the switch. The relay coils will attract the clapper "armature" which will, in turn, touch the contact screw causing current in the 120-volt light bulb. When the switch is opened, the magnets will de-energize, causing the bulb to go out.

4

Miscellaneous Electrical Experiments

In this final chapter, we will present a number of miscellaneous experiments that are interesting and unusual.

THE MERCURY SWITCH

One of the most interesting switches available to the experimenter is the mercury switch. As shown in Fig. 4-1A, the basic mercury switch consists of a glass envelope that contains two metal contacts and a globule of mercury. In the upright position, the mercury is not in contact with the two electrodes, and so the switch is in its "open" or "off" position.

When the mercury switch is tilted as shown in Fig. 4-1B, the blob of mercury shifts so that it bridges the two contacts. Since mercury is an electrical conductor, current is conducted through the contacts. The switch is now in the "closed" or "on" position.

There are a number of interesting applications for the mercury switch. One of the most common applications is the "silent" light switch. In the "off" position, mercury is positioned so that it is not in contact with the contacts. When the switch lever is placed in the ON position, the internal switch is tilted so the mercury makes contact with the contacts.

(A) Open position.

(B) Closed position.

Fig. 4-1. The basic mercury switch.

The experimenter can readily obtain inexpensive mercury switches from most electrical or electronic parts distributors. This switch is supplied with leads for easy interconnection into the external circuit.

Fig. 4-2 shows how the mercury switch can be used as a safety switch for an electric heater. In normal operations, with the heater in the upright position, the mercury switch is also in a horizontal position, and its contacts are closed. Thus, there is current through the heater. Now, should the heater be accidentally knocked over, the mercury switch will be tilted, the contacts will be opened, and current through it and the heater will be interrupted.

If you decide to add this safety feature, use electrical tape to insulate all exposed electrical connections. This safety feature can also be added to devices other than electrical heaters.

Fig. 4-3 shows another application for the mercury switch —a simple burglar alarm. The alarm will sound if the window is opened. As shown, the mercury switch is attached to a small piece of wood. The wood is held in place against the window sill by means of a small spring. The mercury switch

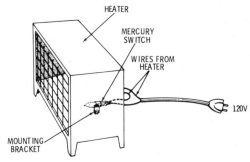

Fig. 4-2. Mercury switch used as heater safety switch.

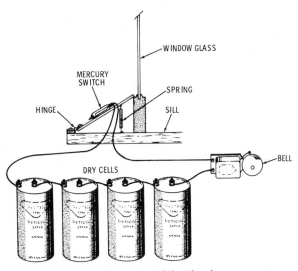

Fig. 4-3. Mercury switch burglar alarm.

is so oriented that with the window closed, the switch is in the "off" position. The contacts of the mercury switch are wired in series with a bell or buzzer and a six-volt battery as shown.

In operation, when the window is opened, the piece of wood drops down to a horizontal position, causing the mercury switch to tilt downward. In turn, this will close the contacts of the switch, and the alarm bell will ring.

THE MAGNETIC REED SWITCH

Another interesting type of switch for the experimenter is the magnetic reed switch. Fig. 4-4 shows the basic magnetic reed switch. Two long metal contacts are encased in a sealed glass tube, and leads to these contacts are brought out through the ends of the tube. Normally, the contacts are separated and the switch is in the OFF position.

Fig. 4-4. Basic magnetic reed switch.

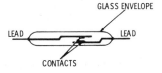

When an external magnet is brought near the glass tube of the reed switch, the magnetic field causes attraction between the two contacts, and they close, placing the switch in the ON position.

There are a number of interesting applications for the magnetic reed switch. Fig. 4-5 shows how the magnetic reed switch can be used as a simple intrusion alarm. The reed switch is mounted on the base of the window by means of either a nonmagnetic bracket, or by a bit of duco cement. A small permanent magnet is mounted on the window. The magnet is positioned directly over the switch so that the reed switch is actuated (contacts closed).

The reed switch is wired through a relay to a bell or buzzer. The relay is a 6-Vac type with spdt contacts. A suitable relay is the Potter and Brumfield KUP5A15. A 6-volt filament transformer powers the relay. A suitable transformer is the Allied 54A1419 or equivalent.

In operation, with the window in the normally closed position, the magnet actuates the reed switch. Thus, the current path is through the switch, relay coil, and the secondary of the filament transformer. The relay is energized, and no current is applied to the warning bell. Should the window be opened, the magnet will move away from the reed switch. This will open the circuit, causing the relay to drop out

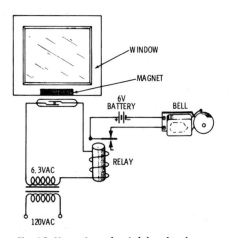

Fig. 4-5. Magnetic reed switch burglar alarm.

(open). The circuit to the alarm bell will be closed; this rings the bell.

This alarm circuit has a rather novel feature, in that it is "fail-safe." That is, should the 120-volt power line be opened, the alarm bell will ring as the relay drops out. Similarly, if the wires to the reed switch are cut, the relay will again drop out, ringing the alarm bell.

Fig. 4-6 shows how the magnetic reed switch can be converted to a sensitive electromagnetic relay. Make a cardboard tube with a diameter just large enough to slip the reed switch into. Make two cardboard washers and cement them to the ends of the cardboard tube. Apply several coats of duco or radio service cement to the cardboard tube and washers to stiffen them.

Wind the core full of No. 24 or No. 26 enamel magnet wire. Bring the ends of the winding out through the small holes punched in one of the cardboard washers.

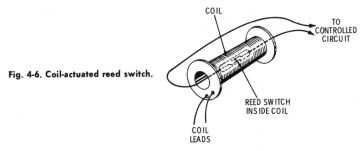

Fig. 4-6. Coil-actuated reed switch.

To operate the relay, place the reed switch into the center of the coil. Connect the circuit to be controlled to the reed switch terminals. The coil can be energized by a 6-volt battery or other low-voltage dc source. Fig. 4-7 shows the setup.

The magnetic reed switch can also be used as a safety interlock switch, as shown in Fig. 4-8. Here, the reed switch is mounted on the inside of the equipment cabinet by means of a small bracket. A small magnet is mounted on the door of the equipment. The contacts of the reed switch are wired in series with the 120-volt power source feeding the equipment.

In operation, when the door of the equipment cabinet is closed, the permanent magnet is next to the reed switch, its

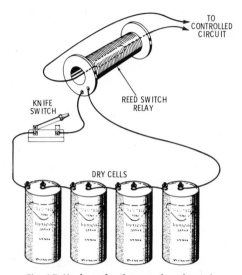

Fig. 4-7. Hookup of coil-actuated reed switch.

contacts close, and power is applied to the equipment. If the door is opened, the magnet is moved away from the reed switch. The reed switch contacts open, removing power from the equipment.

NOTE: If the equipment draws much more than a few hundred watts, a relay should be used in series with the reed switch, because the reed switch contacts will not handle

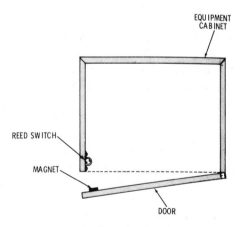

Fig. 4-8. Reed switch safety interlock.

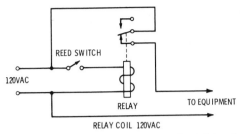

Fig. 4-9. Using a relay in series with the reed switch interlock.

more than a few amperes. Fig. 4-9 shows the setup for using a relay in series with the reed switch.

A SIMPLE WATTMETER

This simple wattmeter is a very handy device for checking the current consumption of various pieces of electrical equipment and appliances. To operate the wattmeter, simply plug the unit that is to be measured into the receptacle and note the meter reading.

Fig. 4-10 shows the schematic of the wattmeter. The device whose current consumption is to be checked is plugged into the receptacle, which is in series with half of the secondary of T1 and the 120-volt line. Thus, the amount of current through the secondary of T1 will be determined by the current drawn by the device plugged into the receptacle.

The amount of current drawn by the load connected in series with the secondary of T1 will be reflected as a voltage across the primary terminals of T1. Thus, the greater the current drawn by the load, the greater is the voltage de-

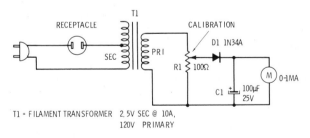

Fig. 4-10. Schematic diagram of a wattmeter.

89

veloped across the primary of T1 and vice versa. As a result, the voltage developed across the primary of T1 is an indication of the load current.

The voltage developed across the primary of T1 is applied to calibration potentiometer R1. The voltage appearing at the slider of R1 is rectified by the half-wave rectifier, consisting of D1 and C1. The resulting dc voltage developed by the half-wave rectifier is applied to indicating meter M.

To calibrate the wattmeter, plug a known load (light bulbs of various wattages will do nicely) into the socket, and plug the line cord into a source of 120 Vac. Assuming the meter scale of 0-1 mA to represent 0-1000 watts, adjust the calibration control for appropriate reading. For example, if a 100-watt light bulb is used as the load, adjust the calibration control for a reading of 0.1 mA, on the meter, and so on.

A DEMONSTRATION CARBON MICROPHONE

This demonstration carbon microphone is similar in design to the first telephone invented by Alexander Graham Bell.

Fig. 4-11 shows how the demonstration carbon microphone is constructed. First, obtain a discarded No. 6 dry cell and disassemble it so as to salvage the carbon rod. After the carbon rod is removed, saw off two sections as shown in Fig. 4-11A. Next, saw a "flat" on each of the two sections of carbon rod and cement these sections to a cigar box. The spacing between the carbon rod "blocks" should be about three inches.

Next, mount the cigar box with the attached carbon blocks to a second cigar box by means of small machine screws and nuts, as shown in Fig. 4-11B. Attach a wire to each carbon block by using tape. Tape a piece of mechanical pencil lead and position it between the two carbon blocks so that it makes a "loose fit."

Finally, connect the leads from the carbon blocks in series with an spst switch, a pair of 2000-ohm headphones, and two series-connected No. 6-dry cells.

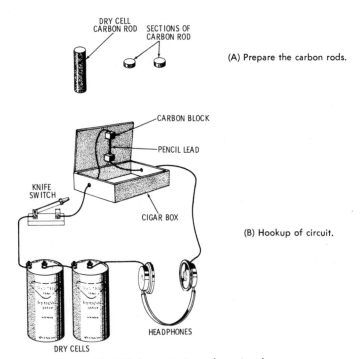

(A) Prepare the carbon rods.

(B) Hookup of circuit.

Fig. 4-11. Demonstration carbon microphone.

To operate the demonstration carbon microphone, place the switch in the ON position. Tap the cigar box lightly with a finger tip and notice how the greatly amplified sound is heard in the headphones. To further demonstrate the amplifying qualities of this microphone, place a watch on the cigar box. You will hear the greatly amplified sound of the watch ticking in the headphones.

Index